ROTHERHAM LIBRARIES AND NEIGHBOURHOOD HUBS

SW

20|6|23

This book must be returned by the date specified at the time of issue as
the DUE DATE FOR RETURN
The loan may be extended (personally, by post, telephone or online) for
a further period, if the book is not required by another reader, by quoting
the barcode / author / title.

Enquiries: 01709 336774

www.rotherham.gov.uk/libraries

Early Readers

'Popping Pam'
An original concept by Jenny Moore
© Jenny Moore 2022

Illustrated by Izzy Evans

Published by MAVERICK ARTS PUBLISHING LTD
Studio 11, City Business Centre, 6 Brighton Road,
Horsham, West Sussex, RH13 5BB
© Maverick Arts Publishing Limited May 2022
+44 (0)1403 256941

A CIP catalogue record for this book is available at the British Library.

ISBN 978-1-84886-880-9

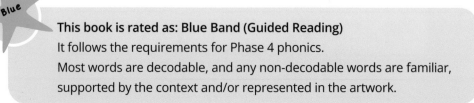

Maverick
publishing
www.maverickbooks.co.uk

This book is rated as: Blue Band (Guided Reading)
It follows the requirements for Phase 4 phonics.
Most words are decodable, and any non-decodable words are familiar,
supported by the context and/or represented in the artwork.

Popping Pam

By **Jenny Moore**

Illustrated by
Izzy Evans

Pam was out for her morning trot.

Clip, clop, clip, clop.

She pricked up her ears.

Boing! Boing! Boing!

"What is that?" said Pam.

Pam had a quick look.

"Wow! That looks good."

"Can I have a go?" said Pam.

"Yes!" said Jen.

"Look at me!" said Pam, with a big grin.

"Look how high I can jump!"

Boing, boing, went Pam,
jumping up and down.

Boing! Boing! POP!

POP!

POP!

"Pam!" said Jen. "Stop popping or the air will come out!"

"Look. It is all flat now," Jen sighed.

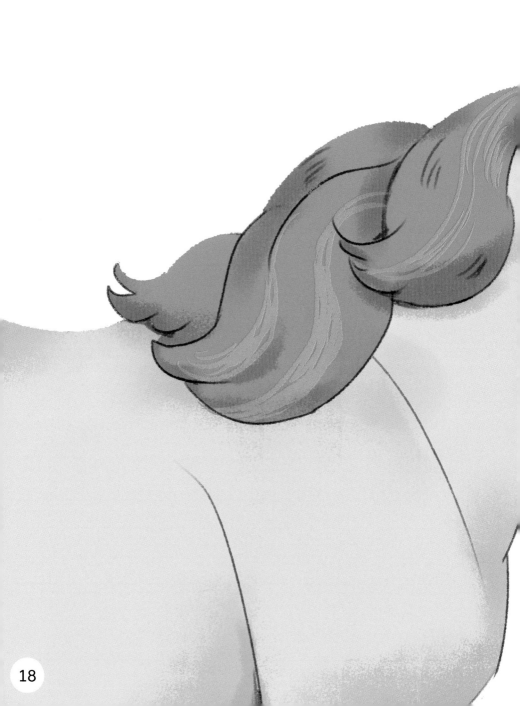

Pam felt bad.

That was the end of jumping.

But then she pricked up her ears.

She had a quick look in the sitting room.

"Wow!" said Pam. "That looks good! Can I join in?"

"Yes," said Jen.

"This is fun!" said Pam.

POP!

POP!

POP! POP!

"Pam!" said Jen. "Stop popping!"

Jen was looking sad. Pam felt bad.

"I will do some **good**

popping for Jen," she said.

Pam got a big pan and some corn.

POP went the corn.

POP! POP! POP!

"Wow!" said Jen. "That popcorn looks good. It smells good too! Keep popping, Pam!"

Quiz

1. What was Pam out for in the morning?
a) A canter
b) A gallop
c) A trot

2. What sound made Pam prick up her ears?
a) Boing!
b) Pop!
c) Bang!

3. Why did Pam have to stop jumping?
a) All the air came out
b) She jumped too high
c) She was too big to jump

4. Why did Pam feel bad?

a) She hurt her leg

b) She ate too much food

c) Jen was looking sad

5. What did Pam pop that was good?

a) Balloons

b) Popcorn

c) Bubble wrap

Turn over for answers

Book Bands for Guided Reading

The Institute of Education book banding system is a scale of colours that reflects the various levels of reading difficulty. The bands are assigned by taking into account the content, the language style, the layout and phonics. Word, phrase and sentence level work is also taken into consideration.

Maverick Early Readers are a bright, attractive range of books covering the pink to white bands. All of these books have been book banded for guided reading to the industry standard and edited by a leading educational consultant.

To view the whole Maverick Readers scheme, visit our website at www.maverickearlyreaders.com

Or scan the QR code above to view our scheme instantly!

Quiz Answers: 1c, 2a, 3a, 4c, 5b